©Éditions Nathan (Paris-France) 1988
English language edition ©Discovery Books 1993

ISBN: 1-55013-476-0

Discovery Books
70 The Esplanade
Toronto, Ontario
Canada M5E 1R2

Printed in Italy

97 6 5 4

My Baby's Album

Illustrated by Joëlle Boucher

DISCOVERY BOOKS

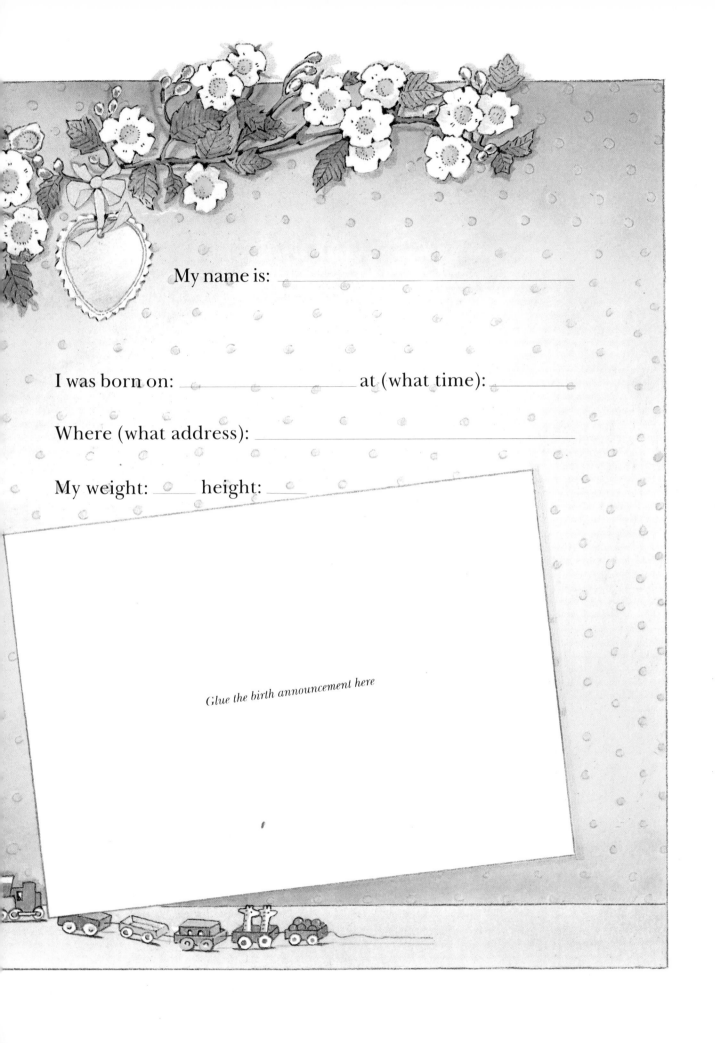

My name is: _____

I was born on: _____ at (what time): _____

Where (what address): _____

My weight: _____ height: _____

Glue the birth announcement here

The way I look

My eye color is: _____

My hair color is: _____

My distinguishing marks:

_____

_____

_____

I look like my daddy

because: _____

_____

_____

_____

My first photos

I look like my mommy

because: _____

_____

_____

_____

What happened in the world on my birthday?

What was the weather like? _____

_____

_____

The big news story: _____

_____

_____

_____

Back home

My address: _____

_____

What's my room like? _____

_____

_____

_____

_____

Who came to see me? _____

_____

_____

My very first presents: _____

_____

_____

_____

My
great-grandparents

My
grandparents

My
parents

My
brother(s) and sister(s)

Me

My first months

My sleep pattern: _____

_____

_____

_____

I sleep

through the night: _____

How many feeds a day?

My first bottle: _____

My appetite: _____

My digestion: _____

Important dates

My first smile: _____

I react to sounds: _____

I suck my thumb: _____

I hold up my head: _____

I hold an object: _____

I look at the object in my hand: _____

I hold my bottle: _____

I eat with a spoon: _____

My first tooth: _____

I sit up by myself: _____

I try to stand up by myself: _____

I eat all by myself: _____

I say Mommy: _____ Daddy: _____

My first tantrum: _____

_____

_____

_____

_____

My first pair of shoes: _____

_____

My health record

My first visit to the pediatrician: _____

_____

Observations: _____

_____

State of health: _____

My first minor illnesses: _____

_____

My immunizations: _____ Dates: _____

_____

_____

_____

(kg)	(lbs.)				
12	24				
11	22				
10	20				
9	18				
8	16				
7	14				
6	12				
5	10				
4	8				
3	6				
2	4				

mos. 0　2　4　6　15　18

(cm)	(ins.)				
80	32				
75	30				
70	28				
65	26				
60	24				
55	22				
50	20				
45	18				

mos. 0　2　4　6　15　18

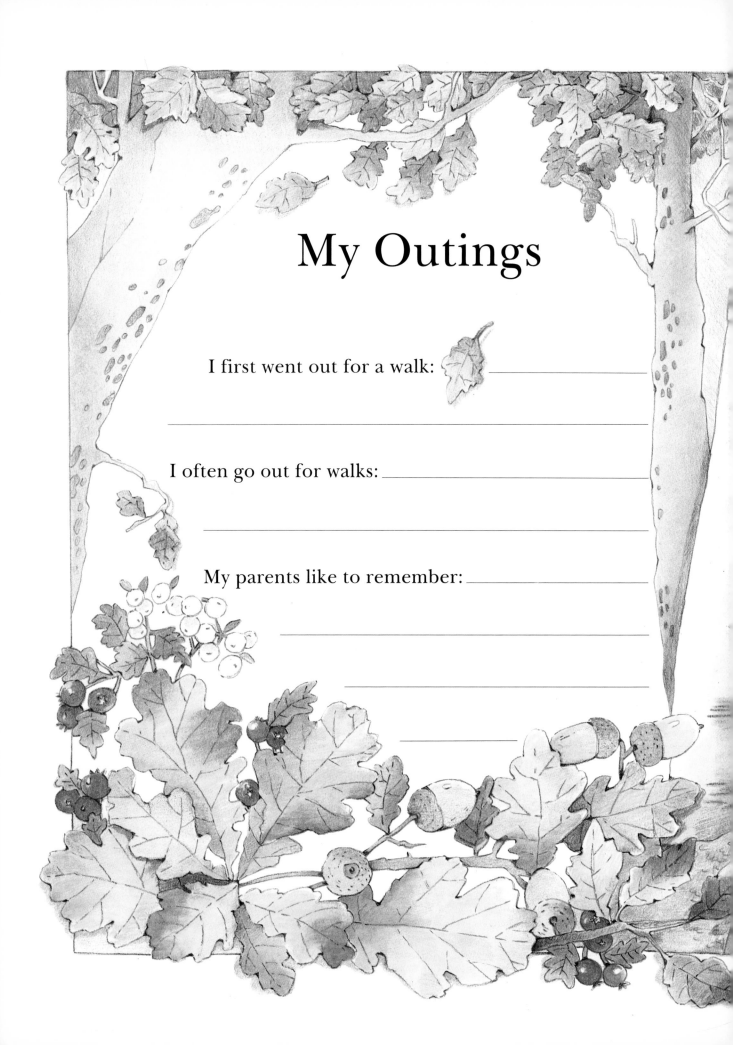

My Outings

I first went out for a walk: _____

_____

I often go out for walks: _____

_____

My parents like to remember: _____

_____

_____

Other outings:

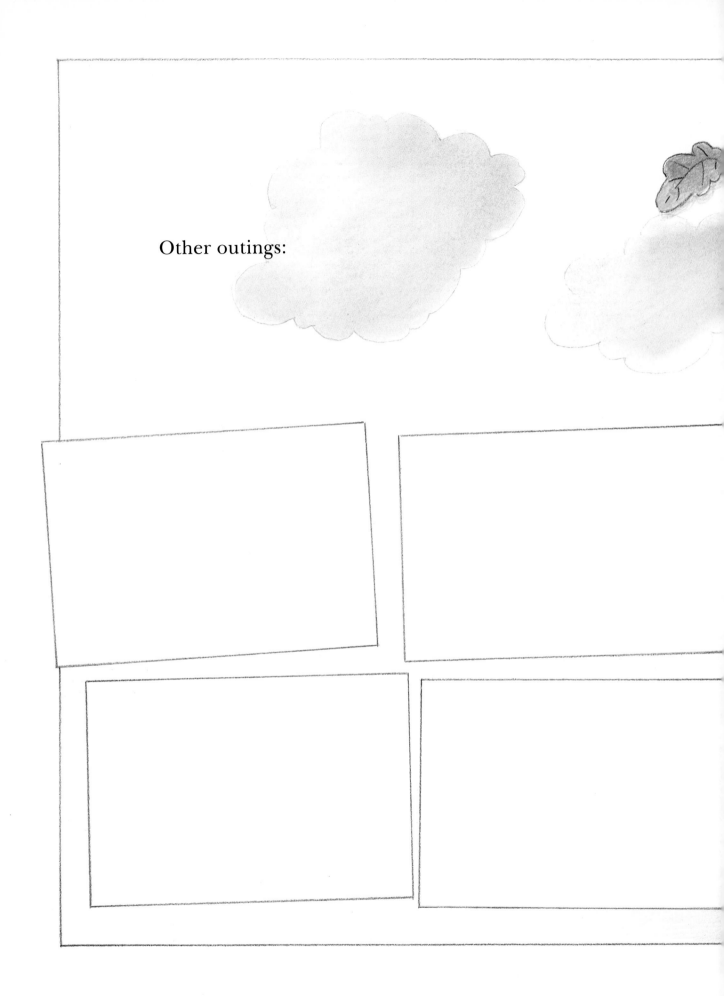

My first Christmas

Celebrated in 19____ Where: _____

With: _____

_____

What was in my stocking? _____

_____

Glue a Christmas photo here

My first birthday

Celebrated at: _____

_____

With: _____

_____

My presents:

Some memories of the day:

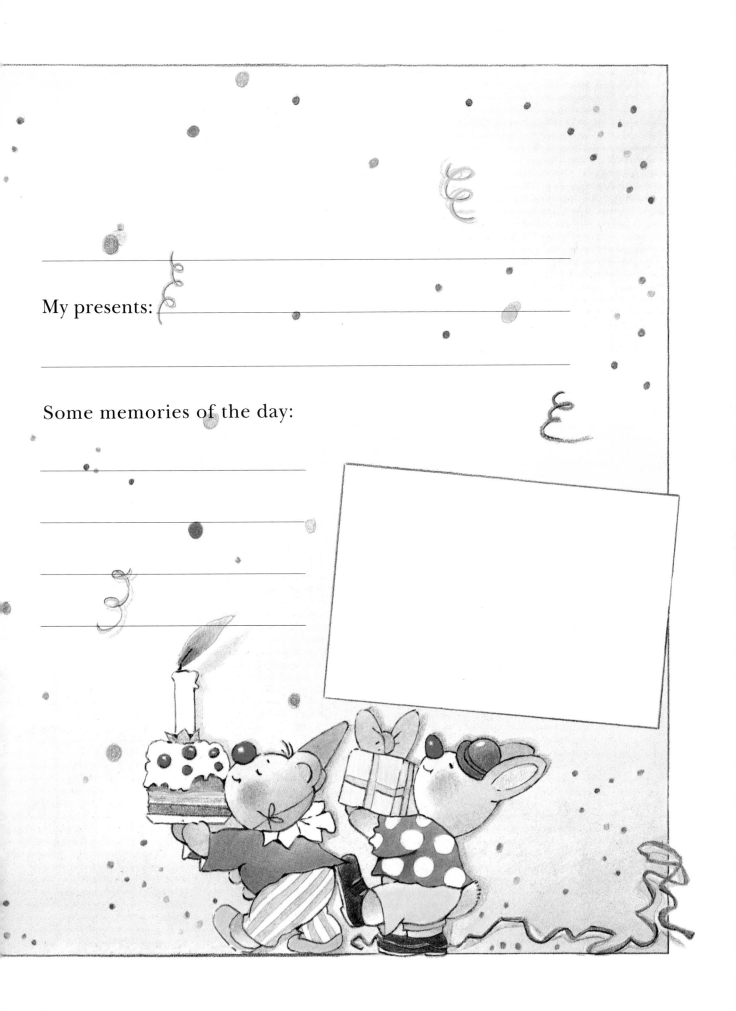

My first steps

I crawled on hands and knees: _____

Standing, holding on: _____

Walking all by myself: _____

Who was I with and where were we? _____

_____

_____

_____

_____

_____

_____

Glue a photo here of my first steps

My first words

My first word-like sounds: _____

_____

_____

_____

_____

My first sentence: _____

_____

_____

My first questions: _____

_____

_____

_____

_____

_____

My favorite expressions: _____

_____

_____

Some funny sentences: _____

_____

_____

Things I know and like

My first favorite song: _____

My first favorite book: _____

Colors I can recognize and name: _____

_____

Animals I like to see: _____

_____

My favorite stories: _____

_____

_____

My favorite meals: _____

_____

My toys — at home, outside: _____

_____

_____

My second birthday

My presents: _____

_____

_____

_____

What my cake was like: _____

_____

Christmas: _____

_____

_____

_____

_____ My presents: _____

_____

_____

_____

My third birthday

I invited: _____

_____

My presents: _____

_____

_____

My cake: _____

_____

I remember: _____

_____

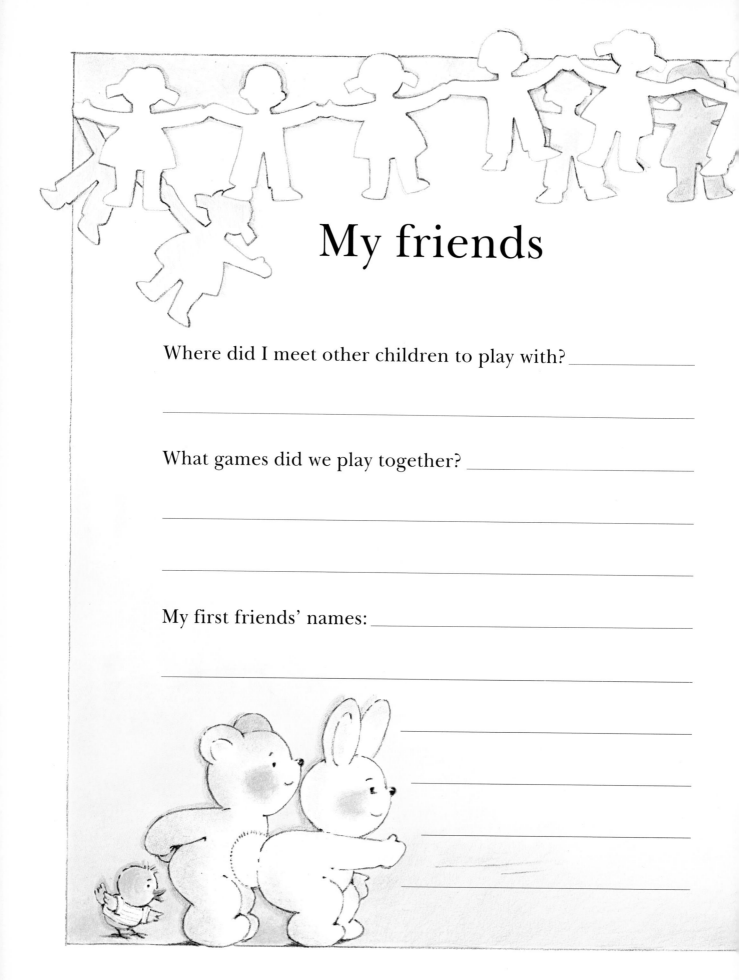

My friends

Where did I meet other children to play with? _____

_____

What games did we play together? _____

_____

_____

My first friends' names: _____

_____

_____

_____

_____

_____

How did we behave with one another? _____

_____

_____

_____

My very first naughty pranks: _____

My first day at school

I started school in (year): _____

Name and address of my school: _____

_____

What happened on the first day? _____

_____

_____

_____

_____

_____

_____

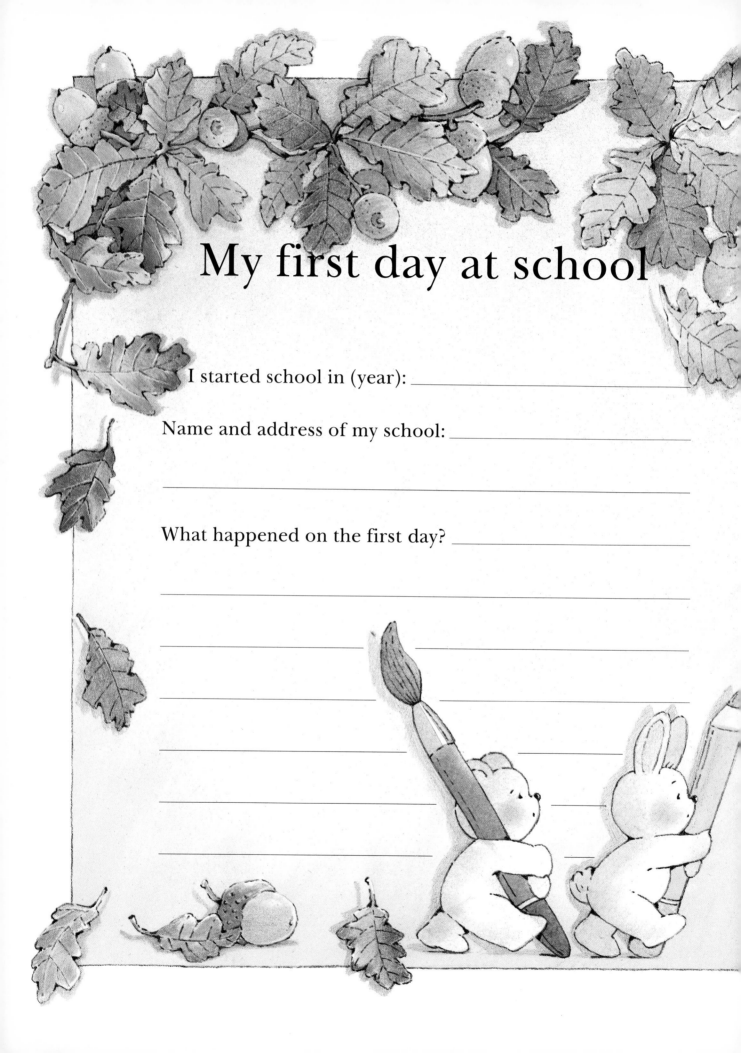

My class photo

My first teacher's name: _____